Emma Poole • Caroline Reynolds • Bob Wo...

ESSENTIALS

Year 9
KS3 Science
Workbook

How to Use this Workbook

A Note to the Teacher

This is the third of three science workbooks for students in Key Stage 3. Together, the workbooks for Years 7, 8 and 9 provide practice of the complete programme of study for Key Stage 3 Science.

This workbook has been written to be used alongside the Key Stage 3 Science Year 9 coursebook. There are four pages of questions for each of the topics in the coursebook. The questions are grouped according to level, to support personalised learning and to enable students to track their own progress.

Included in the centre of the book is a pull-out answer booklet. It contains the answers to all of the questions in this workbook.

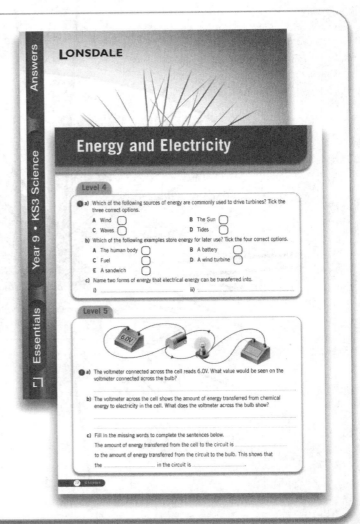

A Note to the Student

We're sure you'll enjoy using this workbook, but follow these helpful hints to make the most of it:

- Try to write answers that require reasoning or explanation in good English, using correct punctuation and good sentence construction. Read what you have written to make sure it makes sense.
- Think carefully when drawing graphs. Always make sure you have accurately labelled your axes and plotted points accurately.

- Where questions require you to make calculations, remember to show your workings. In tests, you might get marks for a correct method even if you arrive at the wrong answer.
- The tick boxes on the Contents page let you track your progress: simply put a tick in the box next to each topic when you're confident that you know it.

Contents

Contents

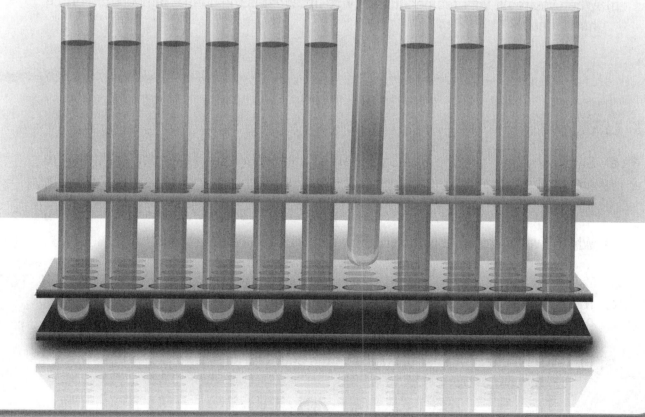

Disruption of Life Processes

Level 4

1 People have been smoking tobacco in Britain for 500 years. But from the 1950s, doctors realised that smoking was the cause of many health problems due to the mixture of chemicals found in tobacco smoke.

a) What is the addictive substance found in tobacco? ....

b) Carbon monoxide is found in tobacco smoke. Red blood cells pick up carbon monoxide more easily than oxygen. Why might this cause the babies of smokers to weigh less at birth than the babies of non-smokers?

....

....

c) Tobacco smoke can cause small tubes (bronchioles) in the lungs to narrow. How might this affect a person who smokes?

....

2 a) Name the three main groups of microorganisms that cause disease in living things.

i) .... **ii)** .... **iii)** ....

b) When you're ill, your temperature may go up. What is the normal temperature of the human body?

....

Level 5

1 a) Substances in glues and paints can cause hallucinations and liver damage if they're breathed in. What are these substances usually called?

....

b) Which two organs are most likely to be damaged by alcohol abuse?

i) .... **ii)** ....

c) If cigarette smoke is drawn through cotton wool, it leaves a brown deposit in the wool.

i) What is this substance? ....

ii) Give one effect of this substance on the body of a smoker.

2 Four people had the percentage level of carbon monoxide in their blood measured at intervals during the day. The table below shows the amount of carbon dioxide (%) in each person's blood at various times on a particular day.

Person	10am	Noon	2pm	4pm
Katie	3.4	2.8	3.5	2.9
Nikesh	6.0	5.1	4.4	3.2
Joe	0.6	0.4	0.4	0.3
Vicki	1.9	1.2	1.1	1.0

a) Joe says he has never smoked a cigarette. Suggest how else carbon monoxide could get into his blood.

_____

b) Which two people are most likely to have smoked tobacco before 10am?

i) _____   ii) _____

c) Katie says she didn't smoke at all during the day. What evidence in the table suggests she isn't telling the truth?

_____

d) Nikesh says he always feels breathless and tired after climbing stairs or doing physical exercise. Use the evidence in the table to suggest a reason for this.

_____

_____

Level 6

1 Freddy came home after school one day and found a slice of pork pie in his school bag. As he was hungry, he ate it. The next day he felt very ill and went to a doctor, who gave him antibiotic tablets for 12 days.

a) Explain why Freddy didn't feel ill until the day after eating the pie.

_____

b) For the next day or so after taking the antibiotics, Freddy felt worse and the number of bacteria in his body still increased. Why did this happen?

_____

c) After taking the antibiotics for 12 days, Freddy had completely recovered. Explain why.

_____

2 Drinking large amounts of alcohol over a long period of time can cause liver damage. The graph below shows the number of deaths from liver disease over a period of time in a European city.

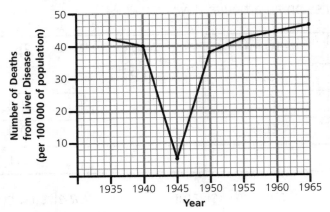

a) Using the graph as evidence, between which years do you think it was hard to get alcohol?

_____

b) Using the graph, what do you think the trend was from 1965 onwards?

_____

c) Alcohol is a drug that affects the nervous system, slowing down the time it takes to react. How would drinking increased amounts of alcohol affect the chances of having an accident?

_____

_____

Level 7

1 Research in Britain has found that heart disease is more common in women in the 60–79 age group than was previously thought. A study of 4000 British women in that age group showed that one in five had signs of heart disease.

a) Why can't this research be used to draw conclusions about heart disease in 60 to 79-year-old women worldwide?

_____

b) Give one reason why the data from this study is likely to be reliable.

_____

c) After reading this information, Charlie said earlier treatments for heart disease must have been a lot more effective than recent ones. Can this statement be supported by the information given? Give a reason for your answer.

_____

_____

2 Cholera is caused by a bacterium. Once in the body, it produces a toxin (poison).

a) Immunity can be gained from cholera using a vaccine containing only a small amount of the toxin. Describe how this injection would give you immunity from cholera.

....

....

b) If a small amount of toxin is placed on a sticking plaster and put onto the skin, the toxin will pass through the skin and help that person to gain immunity from cholera. Why should only a tiny amount of toxin be used?

....

Level 8

1 Viruses consist only of an outer protein wall with some DNA inside. They can only reproduce inside living cells and are unaffected by antibiotics.

a) How can vaccines help the body's natural defences against viruses?

....

....

b) Viruses mutate (change) easily and often to produce a new strain of virus that may have a different protein wall. Give one reason why a vaccine that worked against the old virus might not work against any mutated type.

....

....

2 Sickle cell anaemia is an inherited condition. People who suffer from this condition have mis-shaped red blood cells that look like sickles, or crescent moons, rather than being disc-shaped.

a) The sickle cell shape means that the cell can't carry as much oxygen as a disc-shaped cell. Suggest a reason why this is the case.

....

b) Sickle cells can often 'catch' on each other and become tangled up. Suggest one consequence of this.

....

c) Sickle cell haemoglobin can change into crystals in low oxygen levels. Explain why this would be more likely to happen in blood near to muscle tissue, rather than in blood near to the lungs.

....

Metals and Metal Compounds

Level 4

1 Shaun places a piece of magnesium ribbon into a beaker containing dilute hydrochloric acid, and a chemical reaction takes place.

Beaker

Magnesium ribbon

Dilute hydrochloric acid

a) Suggest one thing that Shaun should do to make his experiment as safe as possible.

....

b) How does Shaun know that a chemical reaction is taking place?

....

c) Complete the word equation below to sum up the reaction that takes place in Shaun's experiment.

.... + hydrochloric acid ⟶ magnesium chloride + hydrogen

d) What sort of substance is magnesium chloride? Tick the correct option.

A An acid ⬭   **B** An alkali ⬭

C A salt ⬭   **D** An element ⬭

E A mixture ⬭

Level 5

1 Calcium chloride can be made by reacting calcium carbonate with an acid.

a) Name the type of acid that should be used in this reaction.

....

b) An excess of calcium carbonate should be used to ensure that all the acid has been used up. Suggest one way of making sure that all the acid has been used up.

....

c) Describe how you could get a sample of pure calcium chloride from the mixture.

....

2 a) Aluminium is a very useful metal. It can be mixed with other metals to form mixtures called alloys. Aluminium alloys can be used to make bike frames. Suggest one reason why aluminium is a suitable metal for making bike frames.

....

b) Copper is used to make saucepans. Suggest one reason why copper is a suitable metal for making saucepans.

....

c) Silver is used to make jewellery. Suggest one reason why silver is a suitable metal for making jewellery.

....

3 Andy adds a solution of potassium hydroxide to a test tube containing dilute hydrochloric acid. One of the products of his experiment is a salt.

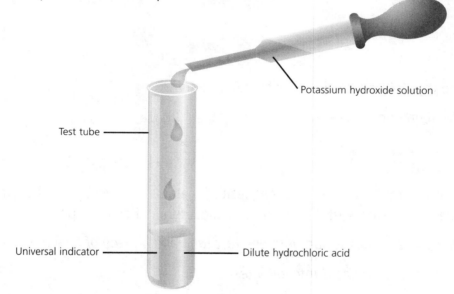

a) What type of chemical is the potassium hydroxide solution? ....

b) Explain how Andy would know when he had added exactly the right amount of potassium hydroxide solution to the dilute hydrochloric acid.

....

c) Although a chemical reaction takes place, Andy doesn't see any bubbles being produced. Explain why he doesn't see any bubbles.

....

d) Suggest why this method of producing potassium salts should be used rather than adding potassium metal directly to an acid.

....

1 Here are two experiments:

Experiment 1

Experiment 2

Copper carbonate — Beaker — Dilute sulfuric acid

Zinc powder — Beaker — Dilute hydrochloric acid

a) i) Give the name of a metallic element used in these experiments. ....

   ii) Give the name of a solid compound used in these experiments. ....

b) In experiment 1, copper carbonate reacts with sulfuric acid to form copper sulfate, water and carbon dioxide. The mass of the contents of the beaker decreases. Explain this decrease in mass.

....

....

c) Complete the word equation below for experiment 2.

zinc + hydrochloric acid ➡ .... + ...

....

2 Kevin was given samples of zinc and magnesium metals. He investigated how the two metals compare when they react with dilute sulfuric acid. Here is Kevin's report:

   1. I put a piece of magnesium into one test tube and a piece of zinc into another test tube.

   2. I put some sulfuric acid into each test tube.

   3. I watched what happened and wrote down what I saw.

a) Give one way in which Kevin made this experiment fair.

....

b) Give two ways in which Kevin could improve his investigation.

   i) ....

   ii) ....

c) What could Kevin observe in his experiment to compare the way in which these two metals react with sulfuric acid?

....

1 The formula for sulfuric acid is H_2SO_4.

a) The element H is hydrogen. Name the other two elements in sulfuric acid:

i) S is _____   ii) O is _____

b) The metal magnesium reacts with sulfuric acid. Complete the word equation below for this reaction.

magnesium + sulfuric acid $\longrightarrow$ _____ +

_____

c) Zinc metal also reacts with sulfuric acid. Complete the symbol equation below to sum up this reaction.

$Zn + H_2SO_4 \longrightarrow$ _____ + _____

1 The table below shows the names and formulae of some useful compounds.

Name of Compound	Formula of Compound
Calcium hydroxide	$Ca(OH)_2$
Sodium hydroxide	NaOH
Sulfuric acid	H_2SO_4
Hydrochloric acid	HCl

a) Calcium hydroxide has the formula $Ca(OH)_2$.

i) How many different elements are represented in this formula? _____

ii) How many atoms are represented in this formula? _____

b) Complete and balance the equation below for the reaction between calcium hydroxide and hydrochloric acid.

$Ca(OH)_2 +$ _____ $HCl \longrightarrow CaCl_2 +$ _____

c) i) Complete and balance the equation below for the reaction between sodium hydroxide and sulfuric acid.

_____ $NaOH + H_2SO_4 \longrightarrow Na_2SO_4 +$ _____

ii) Describe how a sample of pure sodium sulfate, Na_2SO_4, could be obtained from the reaction between sodium hydroxide and sulfuric acid.

_____

_____

Energy and Electricity

Level 4

1 **a)** Which of the following sources of energy are commonly used to drive turbines? Tick the three correct options.

A Wind ◯   **B** The Sun ◯

C Waves ◯   **D** Tides ◯

b) Which of the following examples store energy for later use? Tick the four correct options.

A The human body ◯   **B** A battery ◯

C Fuel ◯   **D** A wind turbine ◯

E A sandwich ◯

c) Name two forms of energy that electrical energy can be transferred into.

i) ....   **ii)** ....

Level 5

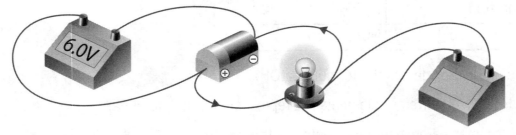

1 **a)** The voltmeter connected across the cell reads 6.0V. What value would be seen on the voltmeter connected across the bulb?

....

b) The voltmeter across the cell shows the amount of energy transferred from chemical energy to electricity in the cell. What does the voltmeter across the bulb show?

....

....

c) Fill in the missing words to complete the sentences below.

The amount of energy transferred from the cell to the circuit is ....

to the amount of energy transferred from the circuit to the bulb. This shows that

the .... in the circuit is ....

2 **a)** What is AC?

_____

Look at the diagrams below.

A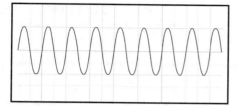

B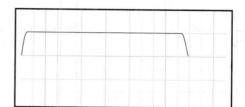

b) Which diagram shows...

i) AC current? _____

ii) DC current? _____

c) Which diagram shows...

i) current from a cell? _____

ii) current from the mains? _____

Level 6

1 The diagram below shows a generator.

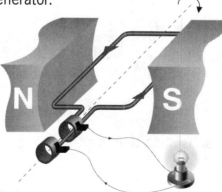

The following sentences describe how a generator in a power station works. Number the stages **1–6** to show the correct order of events.

A The generator produces a current that changes direction every time it turns; this is known as alternating current.

B High pressure steam drives a turbine around and around.

C Steam from boiling water builds up high pressure.

D The turbine drives the generator, rotating a large coil in a magnetic field.

E Fuel or a nuclear reactor is used to heat water.

F The AC current is supplied to your home.

2 a) Complete the table below to show information about a correctly wired plug.

Name of Wire	Colour of Wire Insulation	Description
		A safety wire that connects the metal casing of the device to earth
	Blue	
Live wire		

b) i) When a plug is wired, some of the insulation from the wire is removed before connecting it. Explain why.

ii) Why is it important not to remove more insulation from the wire than necessary?

Level 7

1 a) What is the National Grid?

b) Why do the National Grid cables carry electricity at very high voltages?

c) Explain the purpose of a substation that is close to the generator.

d) Explain the purpose of a substation that is close to factories and homes.

e) Why do houses have electricity meters?

1 The diagram below shows a three-pin plug.

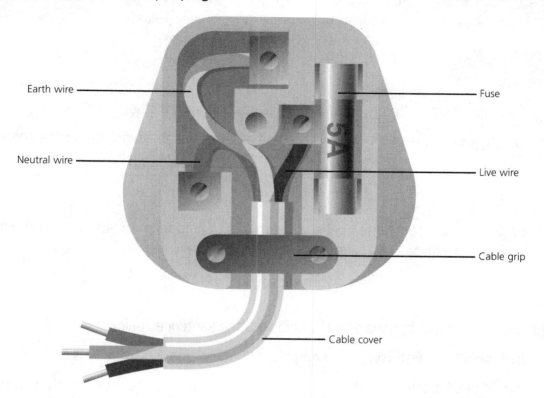

a) Describe how an earth wire should be connected in a device.

b) Explain how the earth wire in a plug works with a fuse to prevent fires and electric shocks.

c) Describe what double insulation is.

d) Explain why the earth wire isn't necessary if an appliance has double insulation.

e) Which method of protection do you think is better: an earth wire or double insulation?

Variety in the Environment

1 Goosegrass grows tightly around other plants such as hawthorn bushes.

   a) Suggest two reasons why this method of growth is an advantage for the goosegrass.

     i) ....

     ii) ....

   b) Plants have specialised cells in their roots to help them to absorb water from the soil. What are these cells called?

   ....

2 Choose from the options given to complete the sentences below.

herbicide   **fertiliser**   **compete**   **pesticide**   **minerals**   **yield**   **territory**

Plants need small amounts of .... for healthy growth. Farmers add

.... to the soil to keep the plants healthy and to increase the

.... Weeds .... with the crop plants, so the farmer

may use a .... to reduce the population.

1 Thousands of trees are cut down in forests every year for human use.

   a) Suggest a reason why fewer small animals and birds can survive in an area where trees have been cut down.

   ....

   b) Give a reason why small plants can grow well in the areas left after trees have been cut down.

   ....

   c) Fungi and bacteria feed on wood that has been left behind after tree cutting and release minerals back into the soil. Why is this an important process?

   ....

   d) Suggest a reason why it's important to plant new trees to replace those that have been cut down.

   ....

2 Maria carried out an experiment with three similar plants. She grew them with their roots in flasks of water and covered different parts with lightproof paper. She then put them on a windowsill in the sunshine.

- Plant A had the flask and roots covered with lightproof paper.

- Plant B had only the leaves and stem covered with lightproof paper.

- Plant C was fully covered with lightproof paper.

a) Plant A grew well, but the other two plants did not. Explain why.

....

....

b) Maria repeated the experiment, but this time she added some soil to each of the flasks of water. The results were the same, but plant A looked much healthier than it did in the first experiment. What could the soil have contained in order to cause this improvement?

....

c) How are roots adapted to take in water?

....

Level 6

1 Victoria had some plants that had pink flowers. She liked the plants so much that she collected the seeds and planted them into pots of soil. She also took some cuttings from the plants and planted them as well. When the plants grew, some of those from seeds had pink flowers, while others had red or white flowers. All the plants grown from the cuttings had pink flowers.

a) Explain why the plants grown from seeds had different coloured flowers.

....

....

b) Explain why the plants grown from cuttings all had pink flowers.

....

c) Suggest two reasons why flower growers grow plants from cuttings.

i) ....

ii) ....

d) Suggest a disadvantage of growing plants from cuttings.

....

2 A farmer's crop was being destroyed by a particular species of caterpillar that was eating it. The following year, he introduced a type of beetle into his crop that he knew ate the caterpillars, and his crop yield was greatly increased.

a) Why did the farmer get a better yield in the second year?

....

b) What is this type of pest control called? ....

c) In the third year, the farmer's crop was reduced again as greenfly attacked his crop. He had seen some of these insects the year before, but they hadn't caused a problem. Suggest a reason why the greenfly were a problem in the third year.

....

....

....

d) Suggest a reason why the farmer didn't use a pesticide to kill the caterpillars.

....

Level 7

1 The graph below shows the population of two species of microbe grown in separate containers.

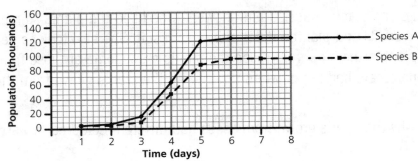

a) When did the population of species A increase most rapidly?

....

b) In their own container, individuals of each species are competing with each other. What evidence is there for this?

....

....

c) Suggest a reason why species B has a lower population maximum than species A.

....

2 Alfie, a farmer, had a problem with his maize crop because it was being eaten by a particular type of insect each year. One year, he decided to experiment. In field A, he planted his usual maize crop and left it untreated. In field B, he planted his usual maize crop but sprayed it regularly with a selective pesticide. In field C, he planted a new type of maize that was said to be resistant to attack from this insect.

a) What is meant by a 'selective pesticide'?

_____

b) Give one reason why Alfie didn't treat the maize in field A.

_____

c) Give one way in which Alfie could tell whether the maize in field C was resistant or not.

_____

d) How could Alfie tell whether the pesticide or the resistant maize was better?

_____

_____

_____

Level 8

1 Dolly the Sheep was the first cloned animal in 1996. She was made by replacing the nucleus of an egg cell from one sheep with the nucleus from a mature body cell of a second sheep.

a) Would Dolly have the characteristics of the egg cell donor sheep or the body cell donor sheep? Give a reason for your answer.

_____

_____

b) Dolly died when she was only six years old, suffering from arthritis and lung disease. These diseases don't usually affect sheep until they're 12 to 16 years old. It was suggested that the cloning caused her early death. Do you think this is true? Give a reason for your answer.

_____

_____

2 A racehorse owner had a champion stallion and a champion mare. He wished to breed a new generation of champions. Suggest two reasons why he might want to use cloning, as well as conventional breeding, to help him to achieve this.

a) _____

b) _____

The Reactivity of Metals

1 The diagrams show an old gold coin and an iron chain. The coin is still shiny after hundreds of years but the iron chain is very rusty after only a few years.

Shiny Gold Coin　　**Very Rusty Iron Chain**

a) The coin is made from pure gold. What type of substance is pure gold? Tick the correct option.

A Element ◯　　**B** Mixture ◯　　**C** Compound ◯　　**D** Alloy ◯

Here are some properties of gold:
- **It's shiny**
- **It's a yellow colour**
- **It has a high melting point**
- **It's quite soft and can be easily scratched**

b) Which of the above properties are generally true of all metals? Circle the two correct answers.

c) Why is the gold coin still shiny after hundreds of years?

_____

d) The iron chain is very rusty. What two things need to be present for iron to rust?

i) _____　　ii) _____

e) Complete the table below to show the properties of the gold and the iron by writing **yes** or **no** in each space.

Properties	The Gold Coin	The Iron Chain
It's magnetic		
It conducts electricity		
It conducts heat		

Level 5

1 Mixtures of metals are called alloys. Some alloys contain a non-metal. Here are some alloys:
- **Stainless steel is an alloy of iron, chromium and nickel**
- **Brass is an alloy of copper and zinc**
- **Steel is an alloy of iron and carbon**

a) Which of these alloys contains a metal and a non-metal? _____

b) Which of these alloys contains two metals? _____

c) Explain why brass doesn't rust. _____

d) Which of these alloys are magnetic? Explain your answer.

_____

2 A copper sulfate solution is made by dissolving crystals of copper sulfate in water. Jamie places an iron nail into a solution of copper sulfate. He observes the reaction that takes place and records his results.

	Solid	Solution
Colour Before the Reaction	Silver-grey	Blue
Colour After the Reaction	Brown	Pale green

Test tube

Copper sulfate solution

Iron nail

a) What type of substance is solid copper sulfate? Tick the correct option.

A Element ◯   **B** Mixture ◯   **C** Compound ◯   **D** Alloy ◯

b) What type of substance is iron? Tick the correct option.

A Element ◯   **B** Mixture ◯   **C** Compound ◯   **D** Alloy ◯

c) Name the brown solid that forms around the iron nail during the experiment.

d) Name the pale green solution that forms in the test tube during the experiment.

3 Sandra investigated how different metals burn in air. First she heated a piece of magnesium metal in a Bunsen burner flame. Then she did the same with a piece of copper metal. Her results are in the table below.

Metal Used	Observations on Heating
Magnesium	Burned with a brilliant white light and produced a white powder
Copper	Glowed red and produced a black solid

a) Give one safety precaution that Sandra should have taken when carrying out this experiment.

b) Name the gas in the air that magnesium reacts with when it burns.

c) Give the symbols for the two metal elements used in this experiment:

i) Magnesium: _____   ii) Copper: _____

d) When copper is burned, the black solid produced is called copper oxide. What type of substance is copper oxide? Tick the correct option.

A Element ◯   **B** Mixture ◯   **C** Compound ◯   **D** Alloy ◯

e) Name the substance produced when magnesium is burned. _____

1 Kieran has samples of four different metals labelled A, B, C and D. He places a piece of each metal into a test tube containing dilute hydrochloric acid and then records his observations. His results are shown in the table below.

Metal	Observations
A	No reaction
B	A few bubbles
C	Lots of bubbles
D	A very vigorous reaction: lots of bubbles and the test tube gets warm

a) Place the four metals into an order of reactivity from the most reactive to the least reactive.

_____

b) When metals react with dilute acids, they produce a gas called hydrogen. Describe the test that Kieran could carry out to confirm that the gas was hydrogen, and the result he would see if it was positive.

i) Test Kieran would carry out: _____

ii) Result if the test was positive: _____

c) Which of the metals Kieran used could be copper? _____

d) Metal D is magnesium. Complete the word equation below to sum up the reaction between magnesium metal and dilute hydrochloric acid.

magnesium + hydrochloric acid ➡ _____ _____ +

_____

2 A section of the reactivity series is shown opposite.

Look at the combinations of chemicals listed below. For each combination, decide whether a displacement reaction would take place or not. If a reaction would take place, complete the **word equation** to sum up the reaction. If no reaction would take place, write **no reaction**.

Most reactive

Magnesium
Aluminium
Zinc
Iron
Copper

Least reactive

a) zinc + copper sulfate ➡ _____

b) aluminium oxide + iron ➡ _____

c) zinc + iron sulfate ➡ _____

d) magnesium sulfate + iron ➡ _____

e) copper + zinc sulfate ➡ _____

Level 7

1 Zinc sulfate is formed when zinc metal reacts with sulfuric acid.

a) Write a word equation to sum up the reaction between zinc and sulfuric acid.

b) Explain why copper sulfate can't be made by adding copper metal to sulfuric acid.

c) Magnesium chloride can be made by reacting magnesium metal with a different dilute acid. Name this acid.

d) The table below shows the formulae of some compounds. Complete the table by naming these compounds.

Formula of Compound	Name of Compound
MgO	
$FeCl_2$	
$CuCO_3$	
$CuSO_4$	
$Zn(NO_3)_2$	

Level 8

1 When copper is heated in air, it reacts with oxygen to form a black solid called copper oxide.

a) What is the formula of copper oxide?

b) Write a balanced symbol equation to sum up this reaction.

c) What type of reaction is this?

d) When a piece of copper weighing 0.56g was heated, its mass increased to 0.74g. Explain why the mass of the copper increased.

Pushing and Turning

1. A tractor is towing a car out of a muddy swamp. The car tyres sink into the mud much deeper than the tractor tyres. Explain why this is the case.

Level 5

1. The block below has dimensions 5cm x 6cm x 8cm. It has a weight of 50N.

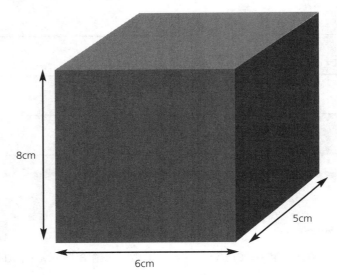

8cm

5cm

6cm

   a) Calculate the maximum pressure that this block could exert on a surface.

   b) Calculate the minimum pressure that this block could exert on a surface.

2. **a)** Explain how a gas exerts pressure on the inside wall of a balloon.

   b) Give one way in which the pressure inside the balloon could be increased.

LONSDALE

ESSENTIALS

Year 9
KS3 Science
Workbook Answers

DISRUPTION OF LIFE PROCESSES

Pages 4–7

Level 4

1. a) Nicotine
   b) In a smoker, there would be less oxygen passing from the mother's blood to the foetus, which would deprive it of oxygen for energy to grow.
   c) The person would become out of breath easily / get tired easily.

2. a) i)–iii) **In any order:** bacteria; fungi; viruses
   b) 37°C

Level 5

1. a) Solvents
   b) i)–ii) **In any order:** liver; brain
   c) i) Tar
   ii) **Any sensible answer, e.g.:** cancer (of a named organ); the cilia (tiny hairs) in the windpipe stop beating, causing mucus build-up and coughing / emphysema.

2. a) **Any sensible answer, e.g.:** from traffic fumes; from passive smoking
   b) i)–ii) **In any order:** Nikesh; Katie
   c) The amount of carbon monoxide in her blood increased from 2.8 to 3.5% between noon and 2pm.
   d) The carbon monoxide levels in his blood are quite high (between 6.0 and 3.2%). This would make him breathless and tired because carbon monoxide reduces the ability of red blood cells to carry oxygen.

Level 6

1. a) The bacteria first had to multiply / grow.
   b) It took time for the antibiotics to work / get into the blood.
   c) All the bacteria had been killed (by the antibiotic).

2. a) 1940–45, as the number of deaths dropped sharply.
   b) It would continue to increase slowly.
   c) It would increase the chances of an accident because the greater the amount of alcohol consumed, the slower the reactions.

Level 7

1. a) The study only investigated British women, and the lifestyles / diets of women in other countries may be different.
   b) It was a large sample (of 4000).
   c) No. There is no evidence (or mention) of any type of treatment.

2. a) The white blood cells would produce antibodies / antitoxins that prevented further infection or destroyed the toxin / bacteria.
   b) So that the person doesn't get cholera / die.

Level 8

1. a) Vaccines are made from weakened / dead viruses that cause the body to produce antibodies / antitoxins. The antibodies / antitoxins then attack viruses that invade the body.
   b) **Any one from:** the vaccine wouldn't contain the right viruses, so the antibodies produced by the body wouldn't recognise a mutated type and wouldn't kill it; the old antibodies wouldn't recognise / attack / kill the new strain of virus if it had a different protein wall.

2. a) The sickle shape means the cell has less surface area / haemoglobin.
   b) **Any one from:** the blood may form a clot; it may block a blood vessel; it may cause a heart attack / stroke.

c) Oxygen is used up (taken from haemoglobin) in the muscle cells, so the oxygen level of the blood is likely to be lower. In contrast, the oxygen level of blood near the lungs is likely to be high.

METALS AND METAL COMPOUNDS

Pages 8–11

Level 4

1. a) **Any sensible answer, e.g.:** wear goggles; tie back hair
   b) He sees bubbles and the beaker gets warmer.
   c) magnesium
   d) C **should be ticked.**

Level 5

1. a) Hydrochloric acid
   b) **Any one from:** add an indicator; use a pH meter.
   c) Filter it, then evaporate the water to leave the salt.

2. a) **Any one from:** it has a low density; the layer of aluminium oxide stops any further reaction.
   b) It's a good conductor of heat.
   c) **Any one from:** it's shiny; it's valuable; it's easy to shape.

3. a) **Any one from:** an alkali; a base
   b) The universal indicator would go green.
   c) No gas is being made.
   d) Potassium is very reactive, so adding the metal directly to dilute acid wouldn't be safe.

Level 6

1. a) i) Zinc
   ii) Copper carbonate
   b) The reaction produces a gas / carbon dioxide, which escapes, so the mass goes down.
   c) zinc chloride; hydrogen

2. a) He used the same method / type of acid.
   b) i)–ii) **Any two from:** use the same volume of acid; use the same concentration of acid; use pieces of metal of the same size.
   c) **Any one from:** he could count the number of bubbles produced; he could measure the temperature increase.

Level 7

1. a) i) sulfur
   ii) oxygen
   b) magnesium sulfate; hydrogen
   c) $ZnSO_4$; H_2

Level 8

1. a) i) Three
   ii) Five
   b) 2; $2H_2O$
   c) i) 2; $2H_2O$
   ii) Use a pH meter to find when exactly the right amount of sulfuric acid has been added. Then evaporate the water to get the sample of pure salt.

ENERGY AND ELECTRICITY

Pages 12–15

Level 4

1. a) A, C **and** D **should be ticked.**
   b) A, B, C **and** E **should be ticked.**
   c) i)–ii) **Any sensible answers, e.g.:** heat; light; sound

Level 5

1. a) 6.0V
   b) The amount of energy transferred from electrical energy to heat and light in the bulb.
   c) equal; energy; conserved

2. a) Alternating current
   b) i) A
   ii) B
   c) i) B
   ii) A

Level 6

1. A5; B3; C2; D4; E1; F6

2. a)

Name of Wire	Colour of Wire Insulation	Description
Earth wire	Green and yellow	A safety wire that connects the metal casing of the device to earth
Neutral wire	Blue	Completes the circuit
Live wire	Brown	Controls the AC current, flowing backwards and forwards many times per second

   b) i) So that the conducting wire can be connected.
   ii) So that the conducting wire doesn't touch the casing of the plug or another wire, which could be dangerous.

Level 7

1. a) A network of cables that sends electricity to towns and cities.
   b) Increasing the voltage decreases the current in the transmission cables. The cables lose less energy to heat when the current is lower.
   c) Substations close to the generator increase the voltage, reducing the energy lost in the transmission cables.
   d) Substations close to factories and homes reduce the voltage to a safer level for industrial and home use.
   e) To measure the amount of electricity they use.

Level 8

1. a) The earth wire should be connected to the metal casing of a device.
   b) The earth wire works with the fuse to protect anyone who uses the device. If a loose wire inside the device touches the metal casing, a large current will immediately flow through the earth wire and the fuse blows. This disconnects the circuit, preventing a possible electric shock or overheating that could cause a fire.
   c) Most modern devices are made of plastic. Since plastic is an electrical insulator, this adds another layer of insulation to it. This is called double insulation.
   d) Appliances with double insulation are already insulated twice because their casing is not made of metal.
   e) Double insulation is safer because an earth wire may come loose, or may not be wired up properly.

VARIETY IN THE ENVIRONMENT

Pages 16–19

Level 4

1. a) i)–ii) **Any two from:** for support; to gain access to more light; to provide protection from herbivores
   b) Root-hair cells

2. minerals; fertiliser; yield; compete; herbicide

Level 5

1. a) **Any one from:** there is less / no food; there are fewer places to nest / shelter; there are fewer places to hide from predators.
   b) **Any one from:** there is more light / water / space / nutrients / minerals; the small plants can photosynthesise more easily; there is less competition from trees.
   c) It provides minerals that the plants need to grow.
   d) **Any one from:** to provide food for animals; to provide shelter / nesting sites / habitats for animals; trees use up carbon dioxide (a greenhouse gas) and produce oxygen; tree roots bind the soil, which helps to prevent the soil eroding / being washed away.

2. a) Leaves need light for photosynthesis. The leaves of plant A weren't covered but the leaves of the other two plants were covered.
   b) Minerals / nutrients / nitrates
   c) They are branched / spread out / have a large surface area / have root-hair cells.

Level 6

1. a) The seeds were formed from sexual reproduction, so the new plants showed variation / had inherited different genes from the parent plants.
   b) They all had identical genes, so they showed no variation.
   c) i)–ii) **In any order:** identical plants can be produced from a single good stock plant; new plants are produced more quickly than from seed.
   d) **Any sensible answer, e.g.:** a disease may affect all plants, not just the weaker ones.

2. a) The beetles ate the caterpillars, so they didn't eat the crop leaves.
   b) Biological control
   c) **Any sensible answer, e.g.:** the beetle had eaten a predator of the greenfly as well as the caterpillars. As a result, there were fewer predators to eat the greenfly, which then reproduced and increased in number.
   d) **Any one from:** he didn't want the chemicals in the pesticide to affect his crop; the pesticide might have got into people who ate the crop plants; the pesticide was too expensive.

Level 7

1. a) Day 3 to 5.
   b) The size of each population reaches a certain level and stops increasing further (the graph lines 'flatten out').
   c) Species B needs more space / food / nutrients than species A.

2. a) A pesticide that only kills one type of pest / insect.
   b) **Any one from:** to use it as a control; to compare it with the other two fields; to check if the other two treatments had any effect.
   c) **Any one from:** he could see if the maize in field C had been attacked by the insect; he could check if the maize yield of field C was greater than that of field A.
   d) He could compare the yields of fields B and C while at the same time comparing the cost of the pesticide with that of the resistant maize.

Level 8

1. a) The body cell donor sheep because this nucleus contained the genes / DNA, whereas the nucleus from the egg cell donor had been removed.
   b) **Any sensible answer, e.g.:** No – there is no evidence to suggest it wasn't just coincidence; Yes – the DNA / chromosomes / genes could have been affected in the cloning process by the physical handling.

2. a)–b) **Any two from:** to produce more offspring quickly; all offspring would have identical genes to the 'parent' horse; he might breed from offspring as well to try to produce an even better horse.

THE REACTIVITY OF METALS

Pages 20–23

Level 4

1. a) A **should be ticked.**
   b) It's shiny; It has a high melting point
   c) Gold is very unreactive.
   d) **i–ii) In any order:** water; oxygen
   e)

Properties	The Gold Coin	The Iron Chain
It's magnetic	No	Yes
It conducts electricity	Yes	Yes
It conducts heat	Yes	Yes

Level 5

1. a) Steel
   b) Brass
   c) It doesn't contain iron.
   d) Stainless steel and steel – they both contain iron.

2. a) C **should be ticked.**
   b) A **should be ticked.**
   c) Copper
   d) Iron sulfate

3. a) **Any sensible answer, e.g.:** wear goggles; tie back hair; use tongs to hold the metal.
   b) Oxygen
   c) **i)** Mg
      ii) Cu
   d) C **should be ticked.**
   e) Magnesium oxide

Level 6

1. a) D, C, B, A
   b) **i)** Put a lighted splint near the gas.
      ii) The gas burns with a squeaky pop.
   c) A
   d) magnesium chloride; hydrogen

2. a) zinc sulfate + copper
   b) No reaction
   c) zinc sulfate + iron
   d) No reaction
   e) No reaction

Level 7

1. a) zinc + sulfuric acid $\longrightarrow$ zinc sulfate + hydrogen
   b) Copper isn't reactive enough.
   c) Hydrochloric acid
   d)

Formula of Compound	Name of Compound
MgO	Magnesium oxide
$FeCl_2$	Iron chloride
$CuCO_3$	Copper carbonate
$CuSO_4$	Copper sulfate
$Zn(NO_3)_2$	Zinc nitrate

Level 8

1. a) CuO
   b) $2Cu + O_2 \longrightarrow 2CuO$
   c) Combustion / oxidation
   d) It combined with oxygen, and oxygen has mass.

PUSHING AND TURNING

Pages 24–27

Level 4

1. The tractor tyres have a much larger surface area than the car tyres, so the pressure is less even though the weight of the tractor may be greater.

Level 5

1. a) $50 / (5 \times 6) = 1.7 N/cm^2$
   b) $50 / (6 \times 8) = 1.04 N/cm^2$

2. a) The gas molecules collide with the inside wall of the balloon, exerting a pressure on it.
   b) **Any one from:** by heating the air inside the balloon; by reducing the volume of the balloon (by squashing it).

3. a) Atmospheric pressure
   b) Because the pressure of the blood in your body is strong enough to balance the atmospheric pressure.

4. Moment = force x distance = 25N x 3.5m = 87.5Nm

Level 6

1. a) The area of the pin point is very small, so the pressure is great and it sticks into the notice board. The area of the pin head is much greater, so the pressure is less and it doesn't stick into your finger. (The force on the pin point and the pin head is the same).
   b) Force = pressure x area = $80N/mm^2$ x $1mm^2$ = 80N
   c) Pressure = force / area = $80N / 40mm^2 = 2N/mm^2$

2. The surface area of the edge of a sharp knife is very small, so the pressure is great. The surface area of the edge of a blunt knife is greater, so the pressure is less.

3. The surface area of the high heels is extremely small, so the pressure is greater. The weight of the elephant may be much greater but it is spread over the greater area of the elephant's feet, so the pressure is less. The greater pressure is more likely to damage the floor.

4. The temperature of the air molecules will increase, increasing the pressure. This is because the molecules gain more kinetic energy and collide more frequently with the tyre walls and with a greater force.

5. a) The wheel
   b) **i)** 600N x 0.3m = 180Nm
      ii) 180Nm / 1.2m = 150N

Level 7

1. a) The centre of the nut (the further the handle of the spanner is from the nut, the greater the turning force or moment).
   b) The centre of the tap (the greater the radius of the tap, the greater the turning force or moment).
   c) The centre of gravity of the high-wire performer (the balance pole is wide, increasing the distance from the pivot, which increases the turning force or moment that the performer can use to keep balance).

2. (600N x 1.5m) / 2m = 450N

3. a) Temperature of (or near) the balloons and size (circumference, radius or diameter) of the balloons.
   b) She must calculate the volume of the balloons.
   c) The greater the temperature, the greater the volume of the balloon.

Level 8

1. a) Liquids aren't compressible, so they can transmit pressure.
   b) The air bubble can be compressed, preventing the transmission of the pressure, and the brakes may not work properly.

2. The pressure of the water would increase as the balloon goes deeper, squashing the air in the balloon, pushing the particles closer together and reducing its volume. The temperature would decrease, reducing the kinetic energy of the particles in the balloon. This would reduce the frequency and force of the collisions of the particles against the wall of the balloon, thus reducing the pressure in the balloon. This would cause the balloon's volume to reduce further.

MANIPULATING THE ENVIRONMENT

Pages 28–31

Level 4

1. a) i) The grower would select seeds from the largest fruits in the original plant and grow them the following year. He / she would then keep repeating the process.
   ii) Selective breeding

2. a) i)–ii) In any order: Long legs – so it can run faster; Strong muscles – to help it run better / to give it stamina to last a race
   b) an egg

Level 5

1. a) A stem cell is an unspecialised cell, but an ordinary cell is specialised for a particular function.
   b) A specialised cell (**or any named specialised cell**)
   c) Using stem cells means destroying / killing the embryo, arguably taking a life.

2. a) A **and** C **should be ticked.**
   b) It could cause the snow / ice in the Arctic and Antarctic to melt, increasing the amount of water in the oceans.
   c) Trees remove carbon dioxide from the air for photosynthesis. So, if they are cut down, carbon dioxide levels aren't reduced as much and the gas stays in the atmosphere, adding to the greenhouse effect.

Level 6

1. a) Any sensible answer, e.g.: the minerals may have been washed into the water from fields where fertiliser has been applied; the minerals may have come from the discharge of sewage from human settlements.
   b) The plants use the minerals to grow.
   c) i) The plants and animals die naturally to begin with, but then decomposer organisms start to use up more and more of the oxygen in the water for respiration. Eventually, the water is starved of oxygen so that nothing can survive.
   ii) Eutrophication
   iii) Any one from: slow release of minerals into the soil; the fertiliser is less easily washed away; fewer minerals dissolve into the rainwater.

Level 7

1. a)

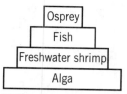

   b) DDT isn't excreted so it's stored in the body. Each animal eats many of the organisms below it in the food chain, so the amount of DDT in an organism increases along the food chain.
   c) i) From the mother's blood (through the placenta or umbilical cord)
   ii) From the mother's milk

2. a) Fewer leaves mean less photosynthesis, so there is less energy in the tree to produce apples.
   b) When the female moths climb up the tree from the soil, they get stuck and can't reach the leaves to lay their eggs.
   c) Many caterpillars and eggs may get eaten by predators or die through disease, so laying a large number of eggs ensures that some do survive.
   d) Any one from: warmth; protection from predators

Level 8

1. a) Photosynthesis
   b) 22 800kJ – 3040kJ = 19 760kJ. **Any reason from:** not all the grass was eaten by the sheep; some grass was eaten by rabbits; some of the grass died; some grass seeds were blown away; the sheep didn't eat the grass roots.
   c) Nutrients (**or a named mineral**) wouldn't be recycled and the amount of grass would decrease, affecting the entire system and its food chains.

ENVIRONMENTAL CHEMISTRY

Pages 32–35

Level 4

1. a) i) Filter paper
   ii) Filter funnel
   b) Filtration
   c) A cross can be placed anywhere on the filter paper.
   d) B **should be ticked.**

Level 5

1. a) B **should be ticked.**
   b) Any sensible answer, e.g.: carbon dioxide; methane; nitrogen oxides
   c) B **should be ticked.**
   d) Any one from: when plants and animals respire; volcanic activity; by burning fuels that contain carbon.

2. a)

Field	pH
A	4.6
B	7.2
C	7.0

   b) i) potatoes
   ii) peas
   iii) carrots

Level 6

1. a) **Any one from:** coal; oil; (natural) gas; peat
    b) S
    c) i) Oxygen
       ii) sulfur + oxygen ➡ sulfur dioxide
    d) Acid rain

2. a) Soil A
    b) She could repeat the experiment using the same soils.
    c) The pH meter is more precise / more accurate.
    d) **Any one from:** acid rain; the rotting of organic material
    e) By adding calcium hydroxide (quicklime) or calcium carbonate (lime)

3. a) Three
    b) D **should be ticked.**
    c) i) C
       ii) **Any sensible answer, e.g.:** oxygen; nitrogen; chlorine; hydrogen
    d) nitrogen + oxygen ➡ nitrogen dioxide

Level 7

1. a) To know what plants to buy / grow.
    b) Soil / flower bed
    c) pH
    d) **Any sensible answer, e.g.:** use the same amounts of soil or water; repeat the experiment; stir the mixtures for the same length of time.
    e)

Soil	pH

Level 8

1. a) $CaCO_3$
    b) $CaCO_3 + 2HCl$ ➡ $CaCl_2 + H_2O + CO_2$

2. a) By lightning
    b) The high temperatures caused by burning fossil fuels in the combustion engine (e.g. cars) allow nitrogen to react with oxygen.

SPEEDING UP, SLOWING DOWN

Pages 36–39

Level 4

1. A and B **should be ticked.**

2. a) 250m/min.
    b) 2cm/min
    c) **Any one from:** 24km/hour; 0.4km/min

Level 5

1. a) i) Downward force of 550N
       ii) Unbalanced
    b) i) Downward force of 300N
       ii) Unbalanced
    c) i) Zero resultant force
       ii) Balanced

Level 6

1. a) Velocity is speed in a particular direction. Speed has no direction.
    b) i) Velocity must take direction into account and the cars are going in different directions.
       ii) 25m/s

2. a) Cheetah = 0.42km/min and dolphin = 0.33km/min, so the cheetah is faster.
    b) Truck = 1 mile/min or 60mph and coach = 55mph, so the truck is faster.

3. B, C and D **should be ticked.**

4. a) It remains stationary.
    b) It continues to move at a constant velocity (constant speed in a straight line).

Level 7

1. a) i) 70N forwards
       ii) Unbalanced
       iii) Yes – the car is accelerating forwards.
    b) i) 30N backwards
       ii) Unbalanced
       iii) Yes – the car is slowing down.
    c) i) 0N
       ii) Balanced
       iii) No – the car is travelling at a constant velocity.

2. a)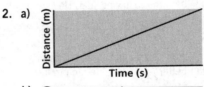
    b)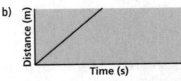
    c)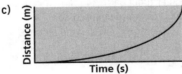

3. a) 100m / 20s = 5m/s
    b) 300m / 60s = 5m/s

Level 8

1. a) The cyclist travels at a constant speed from point A to B. She/he stops between B and C, then continues at a constant speed to D. The cyclist stops again between points D and E. Between E and F, the cyclist travels at a slower constant speed in the opposite direction, ending up at the starting position when she/he reaches point F.
    b)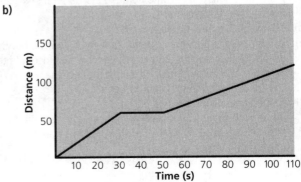

SOCIAL INTERACTION

Pages 40–43

Level 4

1. a) courtship
   b) The Reed Warbler lives in dense reeds and isn't brightly coloured, so it's hard to see.
   c) It helps them to mate and reproduce / have offspring.

2. a) It will prevent the worm from drowning as the burrow fills with water.
   b) The worms come to the surface and are easy to catch to eat.

Level 5

1. a) To keep warm
   b) Because it's very cold on the outside and they take their turn at being cold.
   c) More of them are likely to survive the cold conditions than if they were single or in small groups.

2. The shoal can look like a large fish and this can help to stop many of the small fish being eaten by bigger predators (**'safety in numbers' is not enough as an answer on its own**).

3. a) To attract a mate / male moth.
   b) Male moths may not be close to the female.

4. a) It synchronises the release of sex cells / gametes / eggs and sperm, so that they're all in the water at the same time to increase the chances of fertilisation.
   b) The eggs provide a food source for the fish. Detecting the chemical means they can be present when eggs are released and therefore eat them.

Level 6

1. a) i)–ii) **Any two from:** it provides protection from predators; labour and work functions can be shared; it's easier to find / catch food; it's easier to find a mate / reproduce.
   b) i)–ii) **Any two from:** greater competition between individuals for food; greater competition between individuals for mates; greater competition between individuals for space / living / nests, etc.; 'bullying' of less successful / lower ranking individuals.

2. a) i)–ii) **Any two from:** type A males followed for longer; type B males vibrated their wings for longer; type B males licked for longer; more type B males followed; more type A males vibrated their wings.
   b) Type A because only 70% show first-stage (following) behaviour but the males still achieve the same success rate as type B, of which 82% show first-stage behaviour.

Level 7

1. a) In both percentage response and in time spent in display, the males' response was greater to the red-beaked female than to either of the others.
   b) No – the results only show that the males prefer red-beaked females. They still display to black-beaked females and, to a lesser extent, the grey-beaked type.

Level 8

1. a) Duck B and Duck D
   b) **Any one from:** to make sure the ducks only mate with their own species; the duck wouldn't produce fertile offspring if it mated with a different species.
   c) It shows the male that she is ready to mate.
   d) He can try another female who might be more ready to mate, rather than waste his time on an unresponsive female.

2. a) Species A needs to protect its nest / eggs from predators more than species B.
   b) **Any sensible answer, e.g.:** species B uses more different materials, so it's harder to carry them in the feathers; species B is less likely to drop / lose material; it makes it easier to add material to the nest.

USING CHEMISTRY

Pages 44–47

Level 4

1. a) B **should be ticked.**
   b) Oxygen
   c) A thermometer
   d) 5°C

Level 5

1. a) **Any sensible answer, e.g.:** wear goggles; tie back hair; use tongs to hold the metal.
   b) **Any one from:** there is a change in colour; a new substance is made.
   c) Copper oxide

2. a) **Any one from:** you can see bubbles; the temperature increases.
   b) All the acid / metal is used up.
   c) A **and** E **should be ticked.**
   d) A gas (hydrogen) is made, which escapes.

Level 6

1. a) i)–ii) **In any order:** carbon; hydrogen
   b) 11
   c) hydrogen + oxygen $\longrightarrow$ water (vapour)
   d) Because hydrogen is a fuel and oxygen is needed for things to burn. There is no air / oxygen in space.
   e) **Any one from:** hydrogen is flammable; it could leak and cause an explosion.

2. a) A voltmeter
   b) i) magnesium
      ii) iron
      iii) copper
   c) Magnesium and copper
   d) No voltage because there's no difference in reactivity.

3. a) oxygen; carbon monoxide
   b) carbon + oxygen $\longrightarrow$ carbon dioxide

Level 7

1. a) i)–ii) **In any order:** carbon dioxide; water vapour
   b) $CH_4 + 2O_2 \longrightarrow CO_2 + 2H_2O$
   c) i) It contains unburnt carbon.
      ii) **Any two from:** soot is formed; less energy than expected is released; poisonous carbon monoxide is produced.

Level 8

1. a) i)–ii) **In any order:** carbon; hydrogen
   b) Soot (unburnt carbon) formed by incomplete combustion.
   c) H_2O
   d) Carbon dioxide
   e) 13

SPACE AND GRAVITY

Pages 48–51

Level 4

1. a) i) **Any two small objects, e.g.:** two apples
      ii) Because they have a small mass.
   b) i) **Any two large objects, e.g.:** two planets; a planet and a star; the Moon and the Earth
      ii) Because they have a large mass.

Level 5

1. a) **A planet that is close to the Sun. e.g.:** Mercury, Venus
   b) **A planet that is far from the Sun, e.g.:** Neptune; Uranus
   c) The planets would continue moving in straight lines in the direction that they were going, at a constant velocity.

2. a) 6000 million years
   b) Hydrogen
   c) i) A super nova
      ii) **In any order:** neutron star; black hole

Level 6

1. a) Geocentric model
   b)

Name of Astronomer	Period in History	What they Believed or Proposed
Copernicus	1543	A heliocentric model of the Solar System
Aristotle	400 BC	A geocentric model of the Solar System
Kepler	1609	Elliptical orbits of the planets
Ptolemy	120 AD	A geocentric model of the Solar System

2. a) The force of gravity
   b) The force of gravity
   c) Newton imagined the Moon to be continuously falling towards Earth, but never reaching it. He reasoned that the force of gravity kept the Moon falling and calculated how fast the Moon would have to fall in order to keep orbiting the Earth, but to never reach it.

d) When Newton made measurements of the movement of the Moon, he found that his measurements matched his predictions.

Level 7

1. a) Inside a star, the force of gravity pulls the gases together until the temperature and pressure are so great in the core that nuclear reactions occur. The star changes hydrogen into helium.
   b) If a star is really big it will explode as a super nova instead of becoming a red giant.
   c) A neutron star is a very small, dense star left behind after a super nova (the explosion of a large star). A black hole is formed when an even larger star explodes and the gravity is so strong that not even light can escape.

2. a) i) Inwards (towards the centre)
      ii) His arms
   b) It initially goes in a straight line in the direction it's thrown.

3. a) A squashed circle
   b) Pluto's orbit is so elliptical that sometimes its path comes inside Neptune's orbit.

4. a) They both orbit the Sun.
   b) The comet's orbit is much more elliptical than a planet's orbit. Its distance from the Sun, therefore, varies much more.

Level 8

1. a) Heliocentric model
   b) Telescopes became available and more observations and calculations supported the model.

2. a) Gravity is the force acting on the satellite. It causes it to continually change direction, towards the Earth, so it moves in a circular orbit.
   b) A high orbit satellite has a less curved path than a low orbit satellite, so its speed can be less.

ACKNOWLEDGEMENTS

The authors and publisher are grateful to the copyright holders for permission to use quoted materials and images.

Every effort has been made to trace copyright holders and obtain their permission for the use of copyright material. The authors and publishers will gladly receive information enabling them to rectify any error or omission in subsequent editions. All facts are correct at time of going to press.

Lonsdale
4 Grosvenor Place
London SW1X 7DL

Orders: 015395 64910
Enquiries: 015395 65921
Email: enquiries@lettsandlonsdale.co.uk
Website: www.lettsandlonsdale.com

ISBN: 978-1844-191-352

01/240709

Published by Lonsdale, a division of Huveaux PLC

© 2009 Lonsdale.

British Library Cataloguing in Publication Data.

A CIP record of this book is available from the British Library.

Book Concept and Development: Helen Jacobs
Commissioning Editor: Rebecca Skinner
Authors: Emma Poole, Caroline Reynolds and Bob Woodcock
Project Editor: Richard Toms
Cover Design: Angela English
Inside Concept Design: Helen Jacobs and Sarah Duxbury
Text Design and Layout: Dragon Digital
Artwork: Lonsdale

Printed in Italy

Lonsdale make every effort to ensure that all paper used in our books is made from wood pulp obtained from well-managed forests, controlled sources and recycled wood or fibre.

3 a) The air around you exerts a pressure on you all the time. What is this pressure known as?

b) Why doesn't this pressure crush your body?

4 Calculate the moment of a force of 25N that is 3.5m from the pivot.

Level 6

1 a) Explain why a drawing pin sticks into a notice board instead of into your finger.

b) As a drawing pin point is pressed into a cork notice board, it exerts a pressure of 80N/mm^2 on the board. If the area of the point is 1mm^2, what is the force exerted on the board?

c) The head of the drawing pin has an area of 40mm^2. The force calculated in **b)** is spread over the area of the head of the drawing pin as it is pressed into the notice board. Calculate the pressure on the head of the drawing pin.

2 Explain why it's easier to cut a piece of meat with a sharp knife than with a blunt knife.

3 Explain why a woman in high heels is more likely than an elephant to damage a wooden floor, even though an elephant is much heavier.

4 Describe what will happen to the air molecules in a car tyre, and the pressure exerted by them, when the sun comes out and the temperature increases?

....

....

....

5 Look at the diagram of the wheelbarrow below.

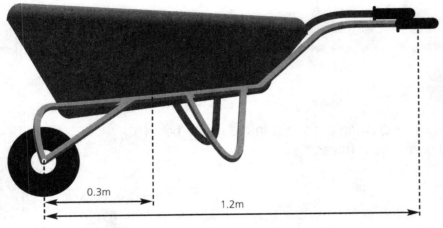

0.3m

1.2m

a) Which part of the wheelbarrow acts as the pivot or fulcrum?

....

b) i) The weight of the load is 600N. Show that the moment of this weight around the pivot is 180Nm.

....

ii) Show that the force needed to lift the wheelbarrow at the handles is 150N.

....

Level 7

1 Moments are used in each of the situations below. Identify where the pivot (or fulcrum) is for each one.

a) A spanner is used to loosen a nut.

....

b) A tap is turned on to fill up a bucket of water.

....

c) A high-wire performer uses a wide balance pole.

....

2 The two children opposite are balanced on a seesaw. Find the weight of the child on the left.

Weight: 600N

2m   1.5m

....

....

....

....

3 Nguyen carries out an experiment to investigate how temperature affects the volume of a gas. She blows up three balloons to the same size. She puts one balloon in the fridge and one on a windowsill in the sun. She leaves the third balloon on the lab bench.

a) What measurements must Nguyen take during her experiment?

....

....

b) What calculation must Nguyen make?

....

c) What result should Nguyen expect?

....

Level 8

1 **a)** Explain why liquids are used instead of gases in a car's hydraulic braking system.

....

b) Why is it dangerous if an air bubble gets into a car's hydraulic braking system?

....

....

2 Explain what would happen to a balloon if it was taken deep into the ocean by a diver. Consider the change in temperature as well as the change in pressure.

....

....

....

....

....

Manipulating the Environment

1 The original wild tomato is believed to have been a small yellow fruit from Mexico. Nowadays, there are thousands of different varieties of tomato, ranging from small cherry to large beefsteak and elongated plum tomatoes.

a) i) Describe how a grower would try to make plants that have larger fruits than the original.

....

....

ii) What is this process called? ....

2 a) Which two features, from the options given below, would a racehorse breeder look for when choosing a horse to breed from? Give a reason for your choices.

Long legs   **Long tail**   **Thick hair**   **Brown eyes**   **Strong muscles**   **Fierce temper**

i) ....

ii) ....

b) Circle the correct option to complete the sentence.

A young foal often has the same colour coat as its mother. This is due to information passed from the mother in **an egg / a sperm / blood / milk**.

1 Stem cells can be found in organs of the body such as bone marrow, muscle and skin. They can also be found in embryo cells.

a) What is the difference between a stem cell and an ordinary cell?

....

....

b) Stem cells taken from an embryo can be treated in a cell growth medium and grown further. What sort of cell will they grow into?

....

c) There is a very vigorous debate about using stem cells from embryos for research. Why is this an area for great argument?

....

2 The greenhouse effect has been slowly increasing the average temperature of the Earth, resulting in global warming.

a) Which of these gases are the main causes of global warming? Tick the two correct options.

A Methane ⬭

B Oxygen ⬭

C Carbon dioxide ⬭

D Sulfur dioxide ⬭

E Hydrogen ⬭

b) Global warming is likely to cause sea levels to rise. Why is this?

....

....

c) Deforestation (cutting down forests) adds to the problem of global warming. Explain why.

....

....

....

Level 6

1 Streams, rivers and lakes may contain a high level of minerals, such as nitrates and phosphates.

a) Suggest why these waters may contain a high level of minerals.

....

....

b) In waters with a high level of minerals, there's often a large amount of plant life. Why is this?

....

c) i) After a long period of time, the plants and then the animals begin to die, leaving the water stagnant. Why does the aquatic life in mineral-rich waters begin to die?

....

....

....

ii) What is the name of this process in the water, from life to death, caused by an excessive amount of minerals?

....

iii) Suggest a reason why using an organic fertiliser would help to reduce this process.

....

1 Scientists used the following food chain from a lake to monitor the amount of an insecticide, DDT, found in the tissues of the organisms.

Alga ⟶ Freshwater shrimp ⟶ Fish ⟶ Osprey

a) Draw a pyramid of numbers for this food chain. Label each section of the pyramid.

The bar chart below shows the concentration of DDT in the four organisms.

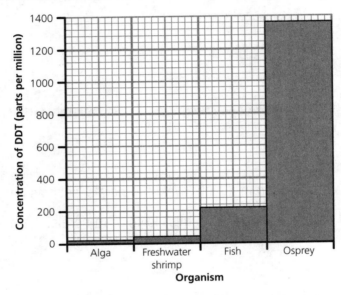

b) Give one reason for the difference in DDT concentration in these organisms.

_____

_____

_____

c) In the 1970s, the average concentration of substances like DDT in harbour seals in northern USA and in Canada was more than 100 parts per million (ppm). A level above 80ppm is considered dangerously high. In the 1970s, many pups died very young due to the high level of chemicals in them. How did these substances get from the body of the mother seal into the pup...

i) before the pup was born?

_____

ii) after the pup was born?

_____

2 Winter moths lay their eggs on the leaves of apple trees. When the eggs hatch, the caterpillars eat the leaves, reducing the yield of apples and possibly allowing other diseases to get into the tree. The caterpillars then go into the soil to pupate and hatch into the next generation of winter moths the following year. The female winter moth can't fly and apple growers reduce moth attacks by tying a sticky grease band around the tree trunk.

a) How does the consumption of the leaves by the caterpillars reduce the yield of apple fruit?

b) How does the grease band reduce the number of caterpillars in the tree?

c) Female moths lay a large number of eggs on the leaves. Suggest a reason for this.

d) Pupating in the soil is better than pupating in the tree. Suggest a reason why.

Level 8

1 The diagram below shows the amount of energy flowing through living organisms in a grassland habitat each year. The numbers are in kilojoules (kJ).

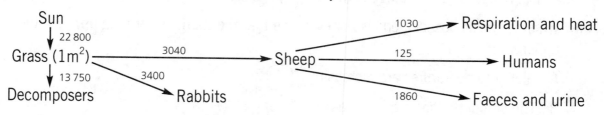

a) How does grass absorb energy from the Sun? Name the process.

b) Calculate the difference between the energy absorbed by the grass and the energy passed on to the sheep. Give a reason for this difference.

c) What would be the effect on the grassland if the decomposers were removed?

Environmental Chemistry

Level 4

1. Duncan is investigating the pH of some soil samples. He places two spatulas of soil into a boiling tube and then adds 5cm^3 of distilled water. He then pours the mixture through the apparatus shown opposite.

   i) _____

   ii) _____

   Mixture of soil and water

   Pipette

   Universal indicator solution

   Beaker

   a) Label the apparatus marked **i)** and **ii)** in the diagram.

   b) What is the name of this separation technique? _____

   c) Put a cross on the diagram to show where the soil collects.

   d) When Duncan adds universal indicator to the solution collected in the beaker, the solution goes red. What type of solution is it? Tick the correct option.

   A Neutral ◯   **B** Acidic ◯   **C** Alkaline ◯

Level 5

1. Scientists believe that the Earth is warming up.

   a) Which of these observations is **not** evidence that the Earth is warming up? Tick the correct option.

   A Global temperatures are increasing ◯

   B The amount of sea ice is increasing ◯

   C Sea levels are rising ◯

   D Winters are getting milder ◯

   b) Name a gas that scientists believe is causing the Earth to warm up. _____

   c) What is causing the Earth to warm up? Tick the correct option.

   A Doppler effect ◯   **B** Greenhouse effect ◯

   C The hole in the ozone layer ◯   **D** Acid rain ◯

   d) Give one way in which carbon dioxide is produced.

2 Ed uses a pH meter to find the pH of the soil in three different fields. He dissolves the soil sample in distilled water and then measures its pH with the pH meter. The soil in field A has a pH of 4.6, the soil in field B has a pH of 7.2 and the soil in field C has a pH of 7.0.

a) Complete the results table below to show the results from Ed's experiment.

Field	pH

b) Ed wants to use the fields to grow potatoes, carrots and peas. Potatoes prefer an acidic soil, carrots prefer a neutral soil and peas prefer an alkaline soil. Which crop should he grow in each field?

   i)   In field A he should grow _____

   ii) In field B he should grow _____

   iii) In field C he should grow _____

Level 6

1 Many fossil fuels contain traces of the element sulfur.

a) Name a fossil fuel. _____

b) What symbol is used to represent the element sulfur? _____

c) When sulfur is burned, it reacts with a gas in the air to form sulfur dioxide.

   i)   Name the gas in the air that the sulfur reacts with. _____

   ii) Give the word equation for the reaction that takes place when sulfur burns.

   _____

d) Name an environmental problem caused by the burning of sulfur.

_____

2 Pauline measures the pH of four different soils using a pH meter. This table shows her results:

Soil	A	B	C	D
pH	4.2	7.2	4.6	6.5

a) Which is the most acidic soil? ....

b) How could Pauline increase the reliability of her results?

....

c) Give an advantage of using a pH meter rather than universal indicator solution to measure the pH of the soil samples.

....

d) Give one reason why a soil might become acidic.

....

e) How could Pauline make a sample of soil less acidic?

....

....

3 Nitrogen dioxide has the formula NO_2.

a) How many atoms are present in one molecule of nitrogen dioxide? ....

b) What type of substance is nitrogen dioxide? Tick the correct option.

   A Element ◯   **B** Mixture ◯

   C Solution ◯   **D** Compound ◯

c) i) Which of these diagrams could represent nitrogen dioxide? ....

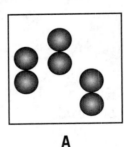 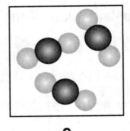 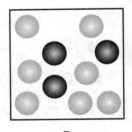

    A   **B**   **C**   **D**

  ii) Suggest the name of a substance that could be represented by diagram A.

....

d) Write a word equation to show how nitrogen dioxide is formed from its elements.

....

1 a) Chloe wants to find out the pH of the soil in different parts of her garden. Why might she want to find this out?

Here is Chloe's report about how she carried out her investigation:

I went around the garden and collected soil from each flower bed. I put a spoonful of soil from each area into separate beakers. I then added some distilled water and mixed the soil and the water. I tested the mixtures using a pH meter.

b) What is the independent variable in Chloe's experiment?

c) What is the dependent variable in Chloe's experiment?

d) How could this experiment be improved?

e) Draw a table that Chloe could use to record the results of her experiment.

1 Limestone, chalk and marble all contain the compound calcium carbonate.

a) What is the formula of calcium carbonate?

b) Limestone, chalk and marble all react with acids. One of the products is calcium chloride, $CaCl_2$. Write a balanced symbol equation for the reaction between calcium carbonate and dilute hydrochloric acid, HCl.

2 Nitrogen oxides can cause acid rain.

a) How can nitrogen oxides be made naturally?

b) How does human activity produce nitrogen oxides?

Speeding Up, Slowing Down

Level 4

1 Which of the following units could be used to measure speed? Tick the two correct options.

A Metres per second ◯   **B** Kilometres per hour ◯

C Seconds per hour ◯   **D** Miles per kilometre ◯

2 Calculate the speed of each of the following. Give your answers in appropriate units.

a) A runner who travels 500m in two minutes.

_____

b) A snail that covers 14cm in seven minutes.

_____

c) A cyclist who travels 12km in 30 minutes.

_____

Level 5

1 Calculate the total (or resultant) **force** acting on each of the following skydivers. Also state whether the forces are **balanced** or **unbalanced** in each case.

a) i) Force: _____

ii) Balanced or unbalanced? _____

Weight: 550N

b) i) Force: _____

ii) Balanced or unbalanced? _____

Air resistance: 250N

Weight: 550N

c) i) Force: _____

ii) Balanced or unbalanced? _____

Air resistance: 550N

Weight: 550N

1 a) What is the difference between speed and velocity?

Look at the two cars below.

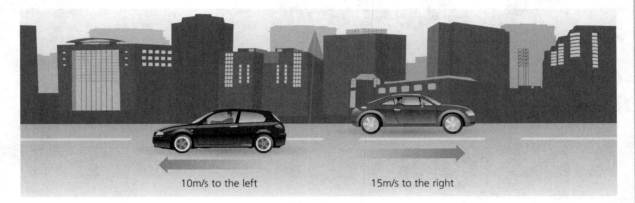

10m/s to the left   15m/s to the right

b) i) A student claims that the difference in velocity between the two cars is 5m/s. Explain why the student is wrong.

ii) What is the correct difference in velocity between the two cars?

2 In each of the following examples, state which has the fastest average velocity.

a) A cheetah that runs a distance of 5km in 12 minutes or a dolphin that swims 500m in 1.5 minutes.

b) A truck that travels 40 miles in 40 minutes or a coach that travels at 55mph.

3 Which of the following events require a force? Tick the three correct options.

A A rocket in space that travels at a constant velocity.

B A marble that rolls along a carpet and is slowed down by friction.

C A racing car that turns a corner at a constant speed of 110mph.

D A ball that is dropped from a window and accelerates under gravity.

4 Describe what happens if there is no force acting on...

a) a stationary object.

b) a moving object.

Level 7

1 Calculate the total (or resultant) **force** acting on each of the following cars. Also state whether the forces are **balanced** or **unbalanced**, and whether the car is **accelerating** or **not**.

a)

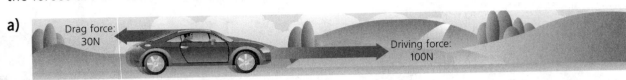

    i) Force: _____

    ii) Balanced or unbalanced? _____

    iii) Accelerating? _____

b)

    i) Force: _____

    ii) Balanced or unbalanced? _____

    iii) Accelerating? _____

c)

    i) Force: _____

    ii) Balanced or unbalanced? _____

    iii) Accelerating? _____

2 Complete the distance–time graphs for each of the following:

    a) A car travelling at a constant velocity.

    b) A plane flying at a constant velocity, much faster than the car in part **a)**.

    c) A car that is accelerating.

3 Calculate the velocity of the cars represented by the following distance–time graphs.

a)

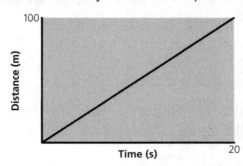

b)

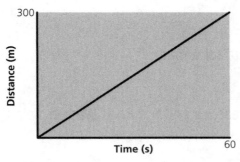

Level 8

1 **a)** Describe the motion of the cyclist represented by the distance–time graph opposite.

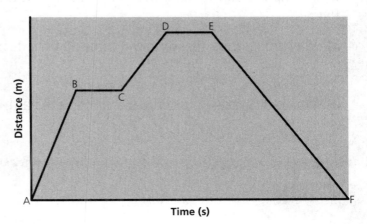

....

....

....

....

....

....

b) Sketch a distance–time graph for a cyclist who travels at a velocity of 2m/s for 30s, stops for a rest for 20s, then continues at a velocity of 1m/s for 60s in the same direction.

Social Interaction

1 The Indian Peacock displays its beautiful, colourful tail to attract a mate. The Reed Warbler isn't brightly coloured, lives in dense reeds and it sings to attract a mate.

a) Displays like those of the Indian Peacock to attract a mate are called

_____ behaviours.

b) Why does the Reed Warbler have to sing to attract a mate?

_____

c) How does behaviour like that of the Indian Peacock and the Reed Warbler help the species to survive?

_____

2 Earthworms live in burrows in the soil. They need air to breathe. Some birds have learned that if they tap the earth near a worm burrow, so that it sounds like rain, the worms will come to the surface.

a) Why do you think the worm will come up from its burrow when it senses the tapping as rainfall?

_____

b) What advantage is it to the bird to tap the earth in this way?

_____

Level 5

1 Emperor Penguins huddle together in the cold of the Antarctic. They take turns at being on the outside of the huddle.

a) Why do the Emperor Penguins huddle together?

_____

b) Why do they take turns at being on the outside?

_____

c) How does the huddling together help Emperor Penguins as a species?

_____

2 Small fish often swim in large shoals in the sea. Suggest a reason why this behaviour might be an advantage to the fish.

_____

_____

3 Many female moths produce a special chemical scent that can be detected by male moths up to 10 kilometres away.

a) Why do the female moths produce this chemical scent?

_____

b) Why do you think the scent needs to be so strong?

_____

4 Sea urchins produce a chemical when they're ready to release eggs and sperm into the water. This causes other sea urchins to release their eggs and sperm into the water.

a) What advantage does this behaviour give the sea urchins?

_____

_____

b) Some fish can detect the chemical produced by sea urchins. How does this help the fish to survive?

_____

_____

Level 6

1 Many animals are solitary, except during courtship. Others may live in societies, such as a troop of baboons or a nest of honey bees.

a) Give two advantages of living in a social group.

i) _____

ii) _____

b) Give two disadvantages of living in a social group.

i) _____

ii) _____

2 In fruit flies, the courtship behaviour first involves the male following the female. The male then vibrates its wings and finally licks the female. The table below shows the percentage of two different types of fruit fly males displaying courtship behaviour and the average time (in seconds) of each display.

Male	Following	Vibrating Wings	Licking
Type A	70% – 4s	24% – 2s	6% – 5s
Type B	82% – 2s	16% – 4s	6% – 7s

a) List two ways in which the behaviour differs between males of type A and B.

i) _____

ii) _____

b) If the female isn't responsive, the male won't continue to the next stage. As shown above, both types are only 6% successful in reaching the final stage. Which type of male is the most likely to mate? Give a reason for your answer.

_____

_____

Level 7

1 In an investigation into courtship behaviour in zebra finches, male finches were caged with a female with a red beak; a female with a black beak; and a model of a female with a grey beak. The behaviour of the male finches was then observed and the results are shown in the graphs.

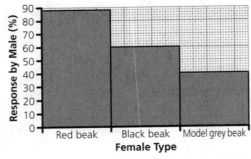

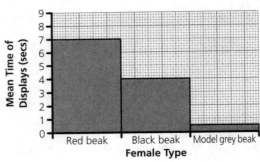

a) What evidence is there that males prefer females with red beaks?

_____

_____

b) Do these results mean that males only mate with red-beaked females? Give a reason for your answer.

_____

_____

Level 8

1. All ducks perform a similar type of courtship display. However, the display movements vary slightly from one species to the next. The order of movements may be different, or some movements may be missed out altogether. The table below shows the display movements of five male ducks.

Duck A	Flicks head	Shakes tail	Shakes beak	Bobs head	Whistles	Turns towards female
Duck B	Shakes tail	Shakes beak	Flicks head	Bobs head	Whistles	Turns towards female
Duck C	Shakes tail	Shakes beak	Flicks head	Whistles	Turns towards female	
Duck D	Shakes tail	Shakes beak	Flicks head	Bobs head	Whistles	Turns towards female
Duck E	Shakes tail	Bobs head	Flicks head	Grunts	Turns towards female	

a) Which two ducks in the table are the same species? ....

b) Ducks display like this in order to recognise their own species. Give one reason why this is so important in courtship.

....

c) If a female selects a male, she will perform certain movements and calls. Suggest a reason why she would do this.

....

d) If the female doesn't respond, the male leaves. Suggest a reason why he gives up rather than tries again.

....

....

2. Lovebirds show different patterns of nesting behaviour. Species A builds a simple nest in the open, while species B builds a more elaborate nest in less-exposed areas.

a) Species A shows much more aggressive behaviour patterns than species B. Suggest a reason for this.

....

b) Species B carries its nesting material in its beak, while species A carries it tucked into its body feathers. Suggest a reason why species B might carry material in its beak, rather than in its feathers like species A.

....

Using Chemistry

Level 4

1 Martin is investigating the amount of energy released when candles are burned. Martin places a boiling tube containing water above a burning candle, as shown opposite.

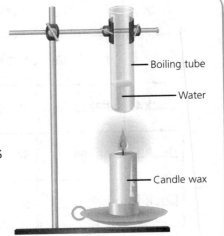

Boiling tube

Water

Candle wax

a) Candle wax is an example of a hydrocarbon fuel. It contains carbon and which other element? Tick the correct option.

A Helium ⬭   **B** Hydrogen ⬭

C Oxygen ⬭   **D** Sulfur ⬭

b) Name the gas in the air that the candle wax reacts with as it burns. _____

c) Martin measures the temperature of the water before and after the candle is burned. Name the piece of apparatus that he should use to measure the temperature of the water.

_____

The table below shows the results of Martin's experiment.

Temperature of the Water Before the Candle is Burned (°C)	Temperature of the Water After the Candle is Burned (°C)
18	23

d) What is the temperature rise of the water in Martin's experiment? _____

Level 5

1 Mickey heats a piece of copper metal in a Bunsen burner flame. The metal glows red and then turns black.

a) Give one safety precaution that Mickey should take when carrying out his experiment.

_____

b) Give one way in which Mickey could tell that a chemical reaction had taken place.

_____

c) What is the name of the black solid formed in Mickey's experiment? _____

2 Jo placed a piece of zinc into a test tube containing dilute sulfuric acid.

a) Give one way in which you can tell that a chemical reaction is taking place.

b) Eventually the reaction stops. Suggest why the reaction eventually stops.

The reaction can be summed up by the word equation:

zinc + sulfuric acid → zinc sulfate + hydrogen

Test tube

Sulfuric acid

Zinc metal

c) What sort of substance is zinc? Tick the two correct options.

A Metal ⬭   B Salt ⬭   C Base ⬭

D Compound ⬭   E Element ⬭   F Mixture ⬭

d) Jo measured the mass of the test tube at the start and at the end of the experiment. She finds that the mass of the test tube has gone down. Suggest why the mass of the test tube has gone down.

Level 6

1 Propane is a useful fuel. It has the formula C_3H_8.

a) Name the two elements present in the compound propane.

i) _____   ii) _____

b) How many atoms are present in one molecule of propane?

c) Hydrogen can also be used as a fuel. It has been used as a fuel for space rockets. Write a word equation to sum up the reaction that takes place when hydrogen is burned.

d) Why do space rockets need to carry supplies of both hydrogen and oxygen?

e) Give one reason why hydrogen has to be stored securely.

2 Adam is measuring the electrical energy produced when two pieces of metal are placed into a lemon. The experiment is shown below along with a section of the reactivity series of metals.

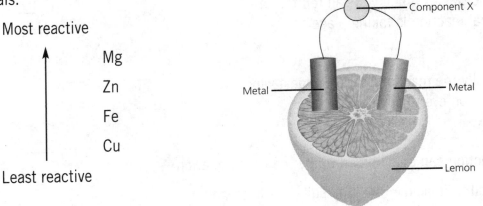

Most reactive

Mg

Zn

Fe

Cu

Least reactive

a) What is component X? ....

b) Zn is the symbol for zinc. Name the other elements whose symbols are shown in the reactivity series of metals above.

   i) Mg is ....

   ii) Fe is ....

   iii) Cu is ....

c) Suggest which metals Adam should use in his experiment to produce the highest voltage.

....

d) Adam repeats the experiment using two pieces of zinc metal. Predict the voltage produced and explain your answer.

....

3 If a fuel that contains carbon is burned in a poor supply of oxygen, incomplete combustion occurs.

a) Complete the word equation below to show what happens in incomplete combustion.

carbon + ... ➡ ....

Complete combustion occurs when a fuel is burned in a good supply of oxygen.

b) Write a word equation to sum up the reaction that takes place during the complete combustion of carbon.

....

1 Methane is the fuel used in Bunsen burners. It has the formula CH_4.

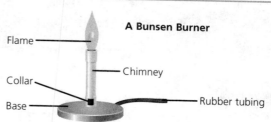

A Bunsen Burner

Flame — Chimney — Collar — Rubber tubing — Base

a) Name the two gases produced when methane is burned in a good supply of oxygen.

i) _____ ii) _____

b) Write a balanced symbol equation to sum up the reaction that takes place when methane is burned in a good supply of oxygen.

_____

c) If the collar on the Bunsen burner is closed, incomplete combustion occurs and the methane burns with a yellow flame.

i) Why is the flame yellow?

_____

ii) Give two reasons why incomplete combustion is undesirable.

_____

_____

1 The diagram opposite shows the apparatus used to test the chemicals produced when butane (C_4H_{10}) is burned.

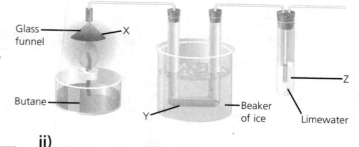

Glass funnel — X — Butane — Y — Beaker of ice — Limewater — Z

a) Name the two elements in butane.

i) _____ ii) _____

b) A black substance forms on the glass funnel at X. What is the name of this substance and how has it been formed?

_____

_____

c) A colourless liquid forms at Y. Give the chemical formula of this substance. _____

d) The limewater at Z turns cloudy. Name the gas that must be present. _____

e) Balance the equation below to sum up the reaction that takes place when butane is burned in a good supply of oxygen.

$$2C_4H_{10} + \underline{\hspace{1cm}} O_2 \longrightarrow 8CO_2 + 10H_2O$$

Space and Gravity

1 **a) i)** Name two objects that have a small force of gravity between them.

    ii) Why is the force of gravity between these objects small?

    b) i) Name two objects that have a large force of gravity between them.

    ii) Why is the force of gravity between these objects large?

Level 5

1 **a)** Name a planet in our Solar System that experiences a large gravitational force from the Sun.

    b) Name a planet in our Solar System that experiences a weak gravitational force from the Sun.

    c) If there were suddenly no gravitational forces from the Sun, describe how the motion of the planets would change.

2 **a)** For how long do scientists expect the Sun to burn?

    b) What fuel is used inside the Sun?

    c) i) Some stars that are larger than the Sun explode. What is this explosion called?

    ii) Fill in the missing words to complete the sentence below.

    After exploding, the star becomes either a

    or a

1 a) What model of the Solar System is represented below?

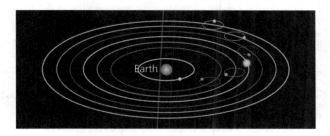

b) Complete the table below about astronomers in history.

Name of Astronomer	Period in History	What they Believed or Proposed
Copernicus		
	400 BC	A geocentric model of the Solar System
		Elliptical orbits of the planets
Ptolemy		A geocentric model of the Solar System

2 a) It's said that Isaac Newton saw an apple falling from a tree. What force caused the apple to fall?

b) Newton claimed that there was a force that kept the Moon in orbit. What is this force?

c) Explain how Newton connected the falling apple and the Moon in its orbit.

d) How did Newton's measurements help him to understand his ideas?

1 a) Describe the chemical reactions that take place in the Sun (a star) and explain how the force of gravity helps these reactions.

b) Why do some stars become red giants and other stars explode as super novas?

c) Explain the difference between a neutron star and a black hole.

2 a) i) When an athlete swings a hammer, what is the direction of the force he is using to keep the hammer swinging in a circular path?

ii) What provides this force?

b) Describe the path of the hammer when the athlete lets go of it.

3 a) The planets have elliptical orbits, not circular orbits, around the Sun. Describe an elliptical orbit.

b) Pluto was the ninth planet of the Solar System until it was reclassified as a 'dwarf planet' in 2006. The average radius of Pluto's orbit is greater than those of the other planets in our Solar System. However, Pluto's orbit is very elliptical. Explain why Pluto is not always further from the Sun than Neptune, the eighth planet in our Solar System.

4 The diagram opposite shows the path of a comet in space. Give one similarity and one difference between a comet's path and the path of a planet.

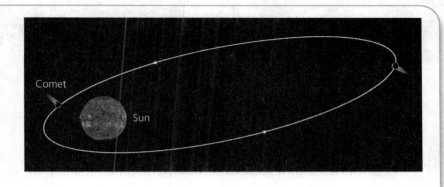

a) Similarity:

_____

b) Difference:

_____

_____

Level 8

1 a) Copernicus suggested a model of the Solar System with the Sun at the centre. The model is represented opposite. What is the name of this model?

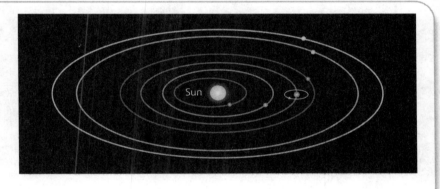

_____

b) Society didn't accept Copernicus's model immediately. Explain what caused society to change its mind and accept this model.

_____

_____

2 a) Once a satellite is in orbit around the Earth, it doesn't need power. Explain what force is acting on the satellite and how this force affects its motion.

_____

_____

b) Why is the speed of a high orbit satellite different from the speed of a low orbit satellite?

_____

_____

Notes

Notes

Periodic Table

Key

H
hydrogen

Atomic Symbol → H
Name → hydrogen

1	2											13	14	15	16	17	18
																	He helium
Li lithium	Be beryllium											B boron	C carbon	N nitrogen	O oxygen	F fluorine	Ne neon
Na sodium	Mg magnesium											Al aluminium	Si silicon	P phosphorus	S sulfur	Cl chlorine	Ar argon
K potassium	Ca calcium	Sc scandium	Ti titanium	V vanadium	Cr chromium	Mn manganese	Fe iron	Co cobalt	Ni nickel	Cu copper	Zn zinc	Ga gallium	Ge germanium	As arsenic	Se selenium	Br bromine	Kr krypton
Rb rubidium	Sr strontium	Y yttrium	Zr zirconium	Nb niobium	Mo molybdenum	Tc technetium	Ru ruthenium	Rh rhodium	Pd palladium	Ag silver	Cd cadmium	In indium	Sn tin	Sb antimony	Te tellurium	I iodine	Xe xenon
Cs caesium	Ba barium	La lanthanum	Hf hafnium	Ta tantalum	W tungsten	Re rhenium	Os osmium	Ir iridium	Pt platinum	Au gold	Hg mercury	Tl thallium	Pb lead	Bi bismuth	Po polonium	At astatine	Rn radon
Fr francium	Ra radium	Ac actinium	Rf rutherfordium	Db dubnium	Sg seaborgium	Bh bohrium	Hs hassium	Mt meitnerium	Ds darmstadtium	Rg roentgenium							